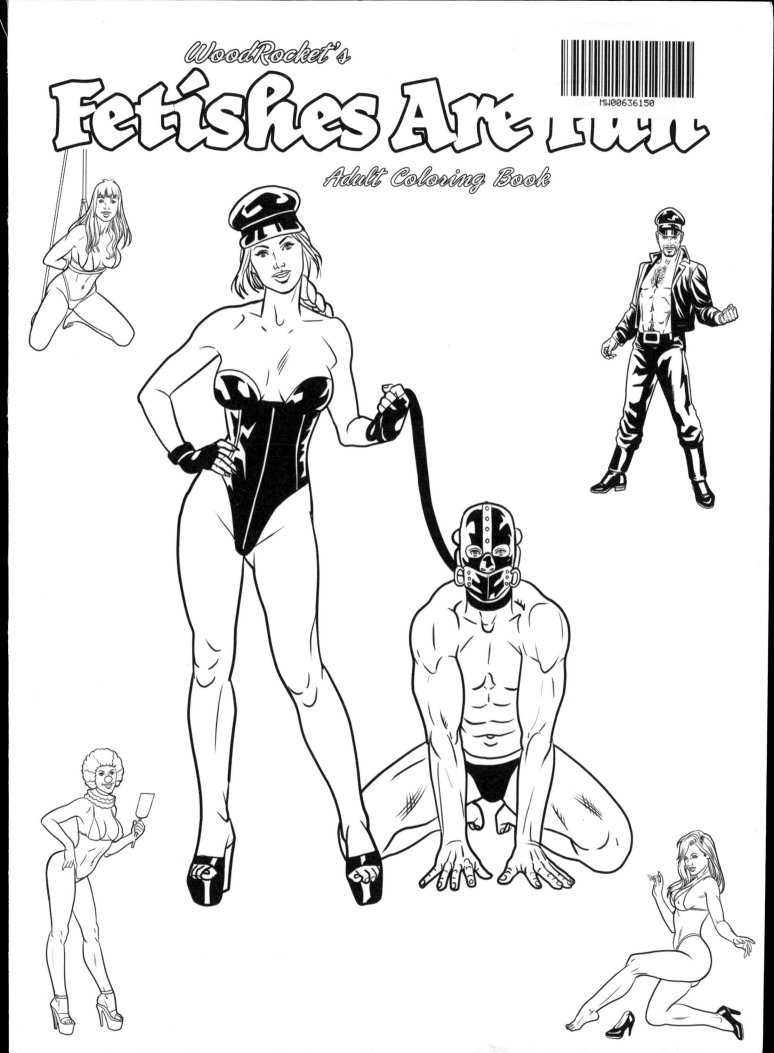

Domination

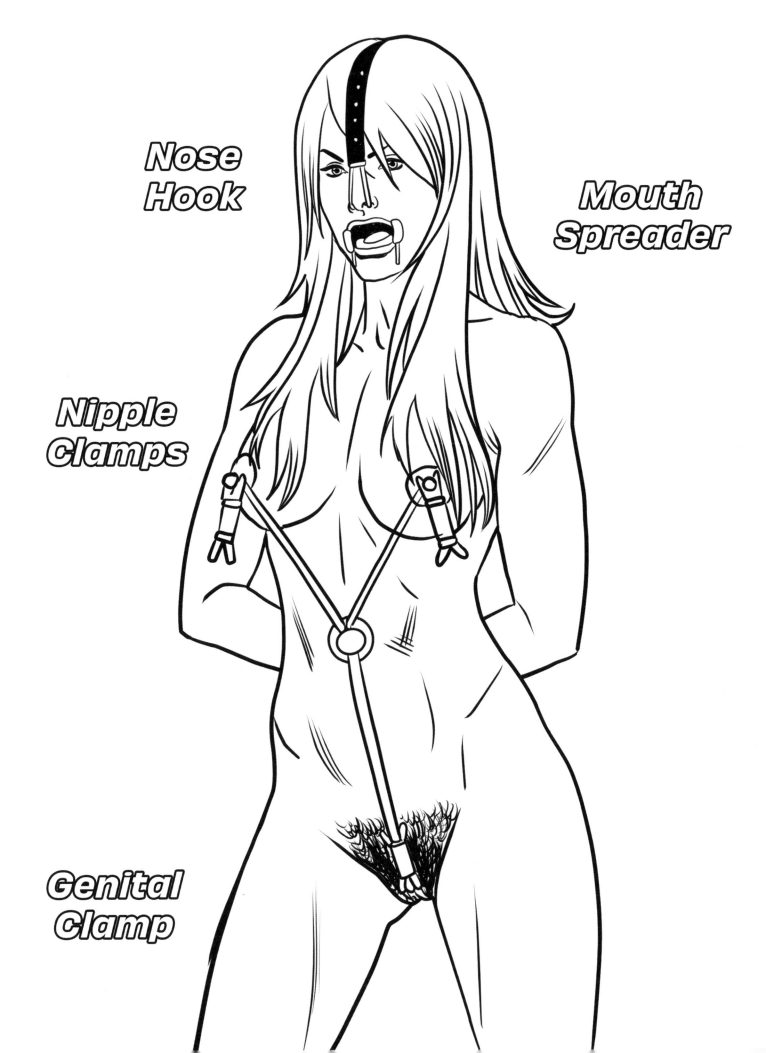

Body Worship

Ass Worship

Balloon Fetish

Looner

Tickling Fetish

Stocks

Hentai

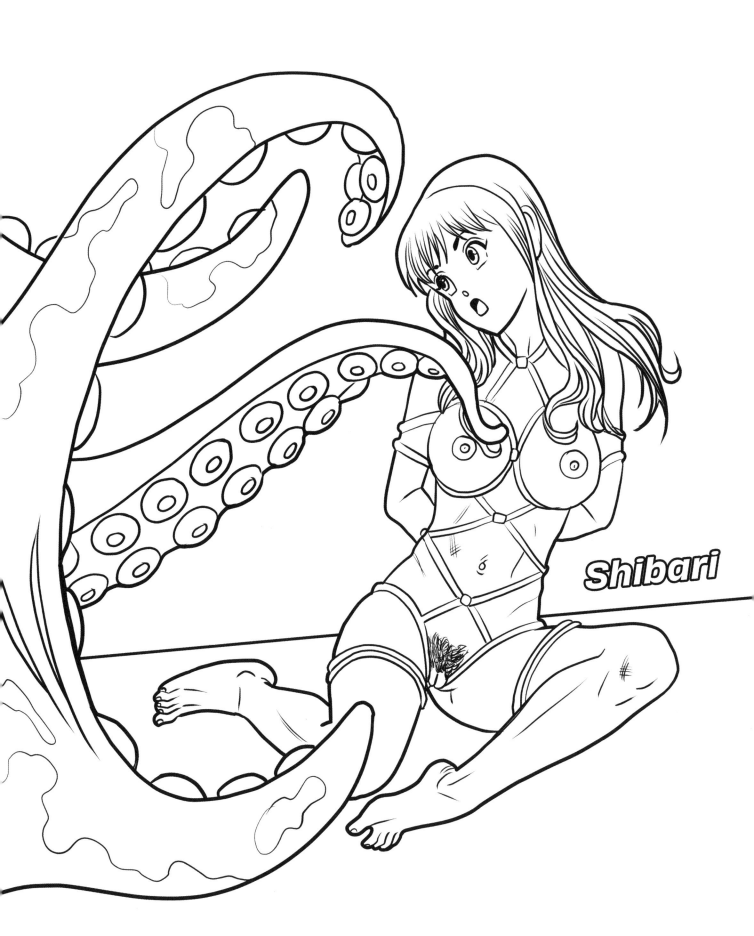

Lace Mask

Latex Mask

Bondage Hood

Furry Mask

Fishnets   **Leather**   **Latex**   **Nylon**

Exhibitionism

Voyeurism

Age Play

Adult Baby Fetish

Spanking

Wax Play

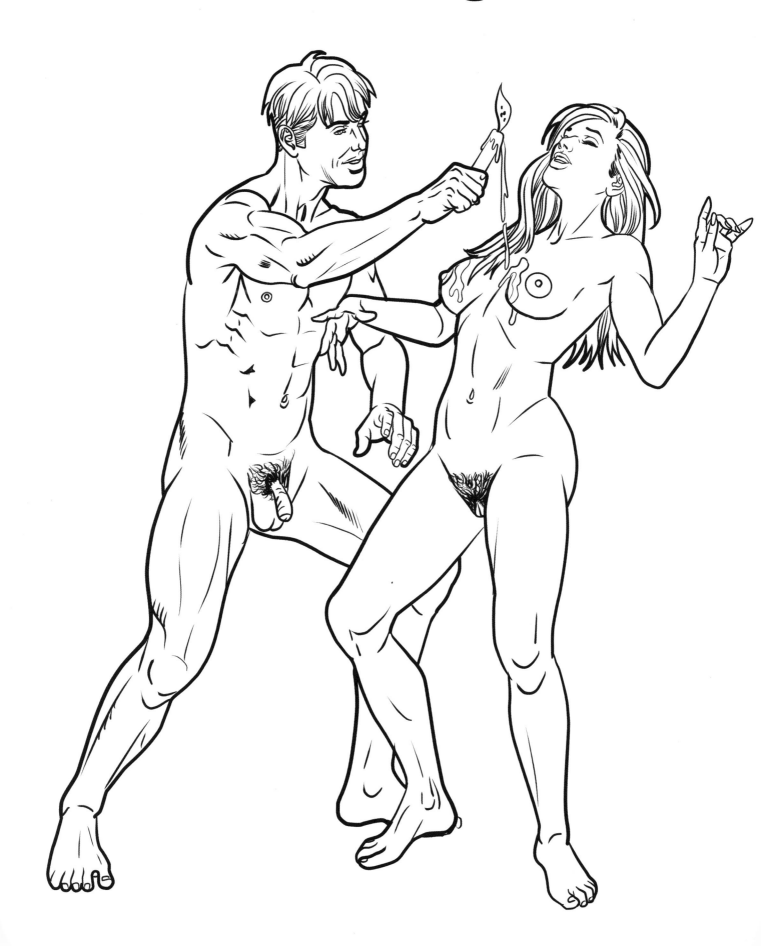

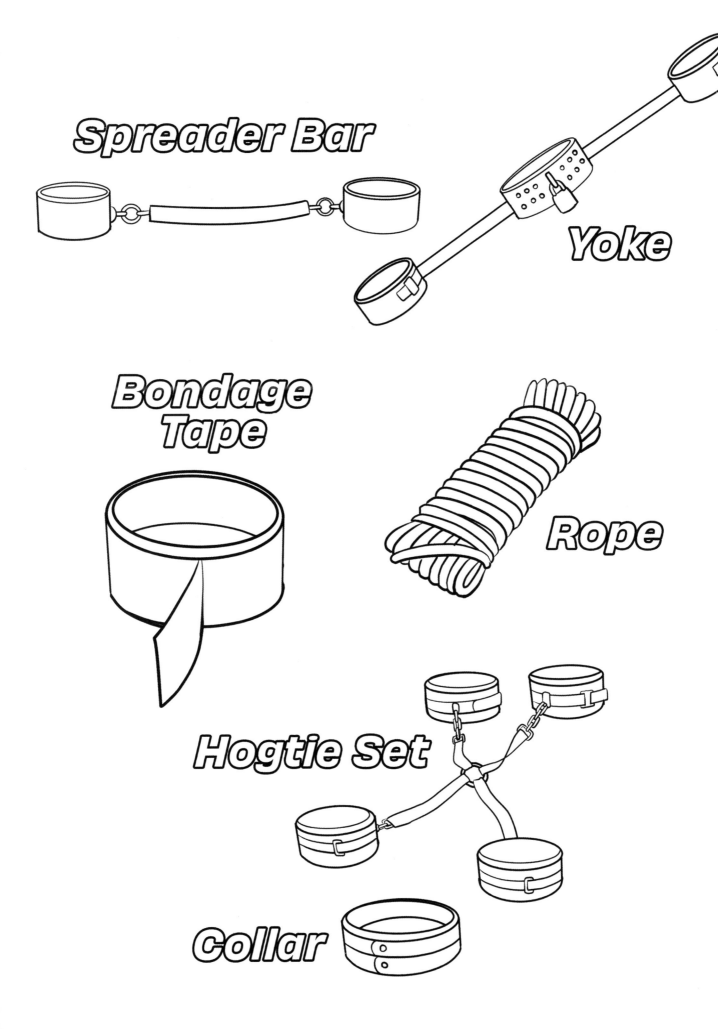

Spreader Bar

Yoke

Bondage Tape

Rope

Hogtie Set

Collar

Flogger Crop Whip Paddle

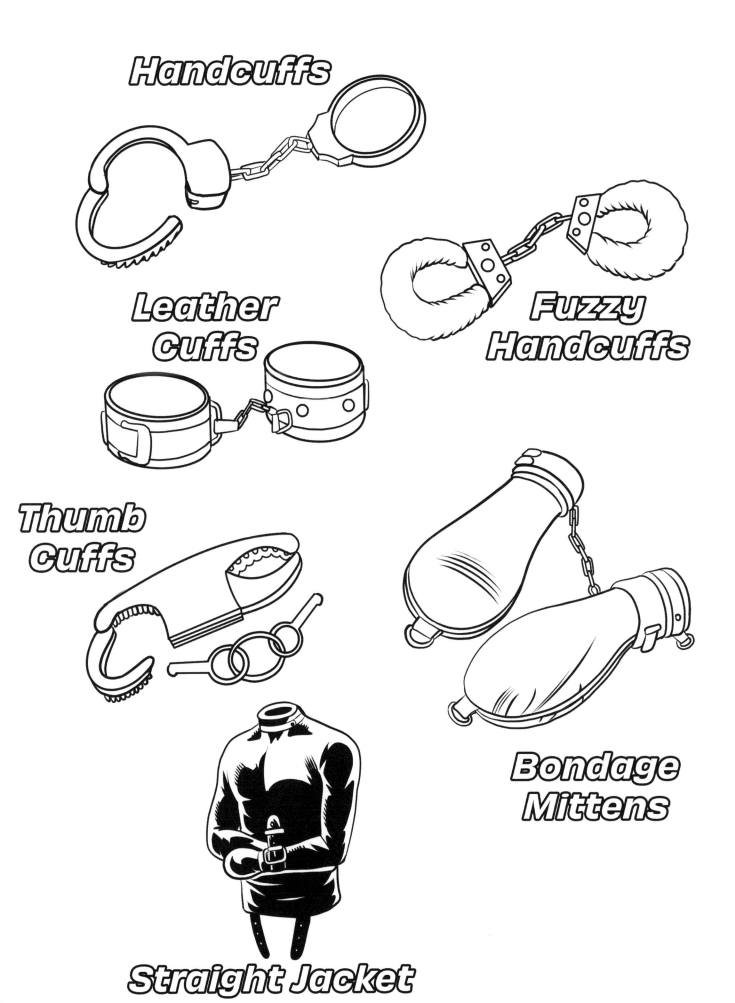

Handcuffs

Leather
Cuffs

Fuzzy
Handcuffs

Thumb
Cuffs

Bondage
Mittens

Straight Jacket

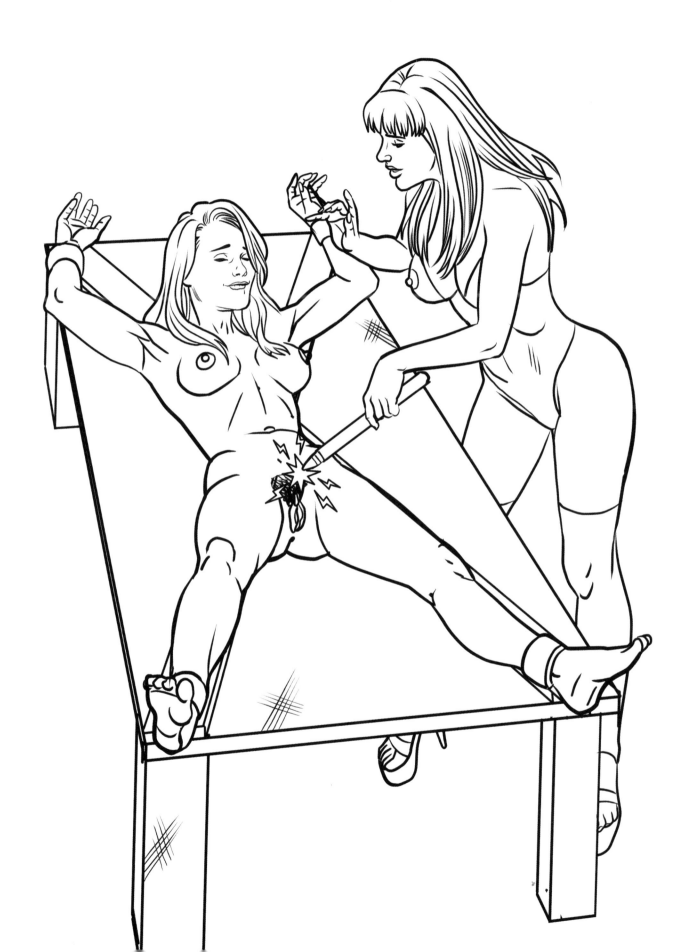

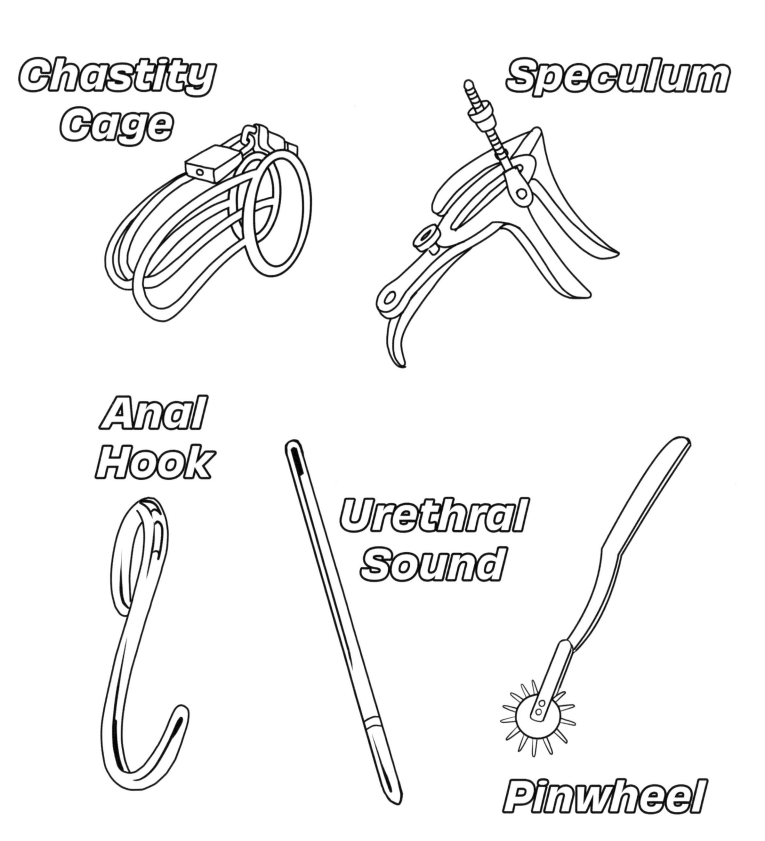

Ballbusting